The Pickpocket Mystery

Elaine Pageler

High Noon Books
Novato, California

Contents

CHAPTER 1

The Chase

Brad Jones and Meg Green worked for the News. They did stories about Riddle Street. But today they went to a flower show. It had nothing to do with the News.

Meg had begged Brad to go. Her Aunt Lill's rose club was having a meeting. It was in her aunt's back yard. They needed someone to take pictures.

So Brad took them. He didn't mind. Taking pictures was something he knew how to do.

Aunt Lill thanked him. "Watch out as you go to your car. There's a pickpocket around here. The police haven't been able to catch him," she said.

Brad nodded. He and Meg started down the sidewalk. His car was parked back on Riddle Street. That was a block away.

"Where's your wallet?" Meg asked.

"It's in my back pocket," Brad told her.

"That's the worst place to keep it. There's a pickpocket. Didn't you hear what Aunt Lill said?" Meg asked.

"No one is going to pick my pocket," Brad told her.

"They might," Meg argued.

They had reached Riddle Street. A market was on the corner. Boxes of fruit sat out in front. An old woman picked out some grapes. She was dressed in a bright red skirt and a yellow blouse. Her purse hung off her arm. It was open. Brad could see the top of her red wallet. It was filled with money.

"See that woman. She's worse than you. Her wallet is easy for a pickpocket," Meg said.

Brad groaned. He knew Meg. She would talk about pickpockets for the rest of the day.

People walked up and down Riddle Street. One young man wore a jacket. Brad thought that was strange. It was warm. No one wore a jacket except a policeman up the street.

Brad turned toward his car. That's when he heard Meg scream.

"Stop thief! That man took the old woman's wallet!" she yelled.

Brad whirled around. He saw a man running down the street. It was the one with the jacket.

"Here, take my camera case. I'll catch him. Go get that policeman," Brad told Meg.

The man had a head start. Even so, Brad was a fast runner. He gained on him.

Then the man ducked into an alley. Brad went after him. The alley ended with a wall. The man began to climb it. Brad grabbed his foot. The man clung to the top and kicked his foot. But Brad hung on.

The man began to climb the wall.
Brad grabbed his feet.

5

"Let me go," the man snarled.

"Give me the wallet," Brad told him.

"What's going on?" a new voice asked.

Brad looked over his shoulder. A young police officer had come up behind him.

"I'm glad to see you. This pickpocket took an old woman's wallet," Brad told him.

The man still clung to the wall. He shook his head. "Officer Pitt, you've got to believe me. This guy started chasing me. So I ran. What else could I do? I thought he might rob me," the man said.

Meg rushed up. "That's not true. I saw the whole thing. This man took a wallet from an old woman," she said.

Officer Pitt looked up at the man on the wall. "Come down, Sly Bragg. Let's see what's in your pockets," he ordered.

Brad turned to the officer. "Do you know him?" he asked.

"Everyone around here knows Sly. He hangs out on Riddle Street all the time," the officer told him.

Sly dropped to the ground. "You won't find anything on me," he said.

"Yes, you will. He took a red wallet," Meg told him.

Officer Pitt went through Sly's clothes. He pulled out some coins and a candy bar. "There's no wallet," he told Brad and Meg.

CHAPTER 2

Questions

Brad and Meg looked at each other. They were shocked. What had happened to the wallet?

Meg looked at Officer Pitt. "I saw Sly take the wallet," she said.

"That may be true. But I can't arrest Sly without the wallet. There's no proof," Officer Pitt told her.

Meg turned to Brad. "Sly took it. I saw him pull the wallet out of her purse. He got rid of it somewhere," she said.

Brad looked at the wall. "Maybe Sly dropped the wallet on the other side. Still I don't know how he did that. His hands were busy hanging on," he said.

"Oh, yeah. I could have hung on with one hand," Sly snapped.

Brad leaped up and caught hold of the top of the wall. He swung himself up. This was the back yard of the market. Boxes had been stacked there. Brad looked down at the bottom of the wall. All he saw was dirt.

"Nothing's here," Brad said. He dropped back down.

"Then he gave it to someone. It must have been while he was running," Meg said.

Brad shook his head. "We ran past a few people. But Sly didn't hand off the wallet. Nor did he drop it along the way. I would have seen that. Maybe he handed it off right at the start. He snatched the wallet. Someone stood close by. He gave it to that person and ran. I would think he had it," Brad said.

"That didn't happen. I was watching. No one was near," Meg said.

Sly grinned. "The truth is I didn't take it. Take your girlfriend to the eye doctor. She's seeing things," he said.

"Meg's not my girlfriend," Brad started to say.

But Sly cut in. "May I go?" he asked.

Brad whirled around to Officer Pitt. "You can't let Sly go. He's a pickpocket. The old woman will tell you the truth," he said.

Officer Pitt nodded. "That makes sense. Come on, Sly. Let's see what the woman has to say," he said.

Sly scowled. Still, he went along. All four of them walked out of the alley. They started for the market.

"Where's the old woman?" Meg asked.

"It's warm. Maybe she's waiting inside," Brad said.

They walked into the market. The grocer was there. But the old woman was nowhere to be seen.

The grocer watched them come in. A look of fear crossed his face. Brad guessed the grocer was afraid of Sly.

"An old woman was outside. Did you see her?" Officer Pitt asked.

"She wore a red skirt and yellow blouse," Meg added.

The grocer shook his head. "I didn't see anyone," he said.

"Why wouldn't she wait?" Meg asked.

"Because you're seeing things, lady. Now may I go?" Sly asked.

Officer Pitt nodded. Then he turned to Brad and Meg. "There's nothing else I can do," he told them.

CHAPTER 3

A Visit with Gertie

Brad and Meg worked on a story for the News the next day. But their minds kept going back to Sly Bragg.

"What did he do with the wallet?" Meg asked again.

"Sly must have dropped it over the wall. Someone was on the other side. That person took it away," Brad said.

"Maybe that's right. But how did he or she know when to be there?" Meg asked.

Brad shook his head. "Who knows? I'll do Aunt Lill's pictures during my noon hour. We can take them to her after work," he said.

Meg smiled. "Thank you," she said.

Aunt Lill was glad to get the pictures. She thanked Brad again.

"We met your pickpocket, Aunt Lill. What do you know about Sly Bragg?" Meg asked.

"Is he the pickpocket? That's no surprise. I always thought he might be guilty," Aunt Lill said.

"Has he lived around here long?" Brad asked.

"No, he moved into an apartment a few blocks away. That was two months ago. The thefts started after that," Aunt Lill said.

Brad told her what had happened yesterday. "Officer Pitt searched him and found nothing. Sly got rid of the wallet somewhere," he said.

"Poor Officer Pitt. He started walking this street a few weeks ago. I'm sure he wants to do well," Aunt Lill said.

"There was another strange thing. The old woman didn't wait to see if Brad caught him. We couldn't find her anywhere," Meg added.

"What did she look like?" Aunt Lill asked.

"She wore a red skirt and a yellow blouse. We asked the grocer who she was. But he didn't know her," Meg said.

"Oh, yes, he did. Everyone knows Gertie,"

Aunt Lill told them.

"Do you know her?" Brad asked.

Aunt Lill smiled. "Gertie has lived in her house for years. She wears that red skirt and yellow blouse most of the time. Everyone knows her red wallet, too. Gertie carries lots of money in it," she said.

"Can you tell us how to get to her house?" Brad asked.

Aunt Lill drew them a map. They thanked her and started off.

Gertie came to the door. She wore her red skirt and yellow blouse.

Brad told her his name. "And this is Meg Green. We saw Sly Bragg take your wallet," he told her.

Gertie's lips grew tight. "You've made a mistake. No one took my wallet," she said.

"Weren't you at the market yesterday?" Meg asked.

Once again, Gertie shook her head.

Meg didn't give up. "It was yesterday. A woman stood in front of the market. She wore a red skirt and yellow blouse. Sly Bragg came up behind her. He snatched her wallet. I know it was you," she said.

"No, you don't. There are lots of skirts and blouses like mine," Gertie said.

"I caught him for you. But he had gotten rid of the wallet," Brad told her.

17

"You should tell Officer Pitt. Then he could arrest Sly. You might get your money back," Meg told her.

"My wallet wasn't stolen," Gertie yelled. She slammed the door in their faces.

Brad and Meg walked back to Aunt Lill's house. They told her what happened.

Aunt Lill phoned the woman. "You're lying, Gertie," she said.

She listened to what Gertie had to say. Then Aunt Lill hung up.

"Gertie's scared. Ed Stone's wallet was taken by Sly. He reported it. Then someone broke the windows of his house. Gertie doesn't want the same thing to happen to her," Aunt Lill said.

CHAPTER 4

Another Theft

Aunt Lill made Brad and Meg another map. This one was to Ed Stone's house. They followed it down Riddle Street.

"Hi," called a voice.

Brad turned. The voice came from Officer Pitt. He was walking down Riddle Street, too.

"How are you two doing? Did you find out who the woman was?" Officer Pitt asked.

"Yes, we did. Meg's aunt knew the woman. Her name is Gertie. She lives around here,"

Brad told him.

Officer Pitt smiled. "Oh, I know her. I guess she does wear red and yellow. But she wears other colors, too. So I never thought of her. Will she fill out a report about Sly?" he asked.

"No, she says that her wallet wasn't taken," Brad said.

Officer Pitt threw up his hands. "That's what's wrong with being a policeman. No reports means no arrests. Thieves can go free. And I can't do anything about it," he said.

"We heard Ed Stone had his wallet taken. He did fill out a report," Brad said.

Officer Pitt nodded. "That's right. It

happened two weeks ago," he said.

Didn't he name Sly Bragg as the thief?" Meg asked.

"That's right. Ed did. But the next day he said it was a mistake. He had found his wallet at home," Officer Pitt said.

"Ed was scared. Someone broke the windows of his house," Meg told him.

A sad look crossed Officer Pitt's face. "I think that's right. But Ed told me something else. He said his windows were old. So he was putting new ones in. That's the trouble. No one will talk," he said.

Brad spotted the market. It had specials on the fruit out in front. So lots of people picked through the boxes.

Officer Pitt went on talking. "You may be right. Sly could be the pickpocket. I wish I knew how to catch him," he said.

Brad looked up. Sly wore his jacket again. He faded into the crowd at the market. Brad couldn't see him now.

"Help! My wallet has been stolen!" a woman screamed. Her voice came from the middle of the crowd.

Officer Pitt blew his whistle. Then he ran to the crowd. "Everyone stay where you are!" he ordered.

Brad raced after him. So did Meg. She was just a few feet behind.

"Help! My wallet has been stolen!"

All the people froze in their places. The woman stood in the middle. She clutched her handbag to her chest. The grocer waited close by. He had a bag of apples in one hand. Several people stood close to her. Sly was off to one side.

Officer Pitt rushed to the woman. "Did you see who took your wallet?" he asked.

The woman shook her head. "I was buying apples. I reached in my purse for my wallet. It was gone," she said.

"Are you sure it was taken in front of the market?" Officer Pitt asked.

"Yes, I checked my money. That was just before I picked out the apples," the woman said.

"O.K., get in line. I'll need to search everyone," Officer Pitt said.

"Start with Sly. He has the wallet," Brad told him.

Sly sneered. "You won't find anything," he said.

Officer Pitt searched Sly. Then he turned to Brad. "He doesn't have the wallet."

Sly smirked. "May I go?" he asked.

Officer Pitt nodded. He turned to search the others. They didn't have the wallet either.

"The woman is sure that her wallet was taken here. So where did it go?" Meg asked.

"Sly got rid of it somewhere," Brad said.

Officer Pit nodded. "But where?" he asked.

CHAPTER 5

Meg Goes Undercover

All the people left the market. But Brad and Meg stayed. They looked through the boxes. Sly could have tossed the wallet in one of them. It would be easy to do.

"We might not catch the thief. But we could give the wallet back to the woman," Meg said.

"It would help catch the pickpocket. Sly didn't wear gloves. So his fingerprints could be on the wallet," Brad told her.

"That's true," Meg said.

The grocer came out of the market. "May I help you?" he asked.

Brad told them what they were doing. "Did you see anything this afternoon?" he asked.

"I didn't see a thing," the grocer said. He turned and hurried back inside.

Brad and Meg went on searching. But they didn't find the wallet.

Officer Pitt had walked over to the woman's car. The two of them were talking. Now he came back. A paper was in his hands.

"Now I have one report. But it doesn't help. She didn't see who did it. And I couldn't find the wallet on anyone," Officer Pitt said.

Meg looked up at the officer. "What would

it take to arrest Sly?" she asked.

Officer Pitt thought for a minute. "The best thing is to find the stolen things on him," he said.

"That hasn't worked. Sly took the first wallet. But we couldn't find it on him. So what else would we need?" Meg asked.

"That's easy. We need a brave and alert person whose wallet was taken. She or he needs to know who took it. Then that person has to be brave enough to fill out the report," Brad told her.

Officer Pitt nodded. "That's right. Where will we find a person like that?" he asked.

Meg raised her hand. "Right here. I'll be your old woman," she said.

"Meg, you can't do that. Sly knows you," Brad told her.

"He won't know me. Aunt Lill used to act in plays. She knows all about makeup," Meg said.

Brad looked at Officer Pitt. "What do you think?" he asked.

"It just might work. Meg is willing. So let's give it a try. Maybe we can catch Sly after all," he told them.

"All the thefts seem to happen in front of the market. So that's where I'll be. But I want you close," Meg said.

"You've got it," Brad promised.

The next afternoon Meg went to Aunt

Lill's. Brad waited in his car. He had parked it across from the market. Officer Pitt was down the street.

Brad was wearing a two-way radio. Officer Pitt had given it to him. Meg wore the other one. That way they could talk to each other.

A woman walked into the market. She looked old and rich. Her open purse was slung over her shoulder. Could that be Meg?

"Is that you, Meg?" Brad said into his radio.

"No, this is a little old woman who's going shopping," came Meg's voice.

Brad laughed. "You're great," he said.

Meg went on to the market. She leaned

over each box and looked at the fruit. Brad could see her fat wallet. It poked out of her purse. That should tempt Sly.

Brad shot a fast glance at Officer Pitt. The officer grinned. He gave him a thumbs up sign.

The grocer was still having specials. So people had stopped at the market. Then Brad saw Sly. He was standing in a doorway. His eyes were on Meg's purse.

Brad spoke into his radio. "Get ready, Meg. Sly has spotted you. He's walking your way. Now he's right behind you. Don't turn yet. He should be reaching in your purse right now," Brad said.

Then Brad couldn't see. Another person

had stepped into his view. Brad jumped out of the car and started running. Officer Pitt raced forward, too. They both reached Meg at the same time.

"Did he take it?" Brad asked.

Meg shook her head. "My wallet is still in my purse," she said.

Brad looked down the street. Sly was standing a block away. It was hard to see for sure. But it looked like a grin on his face.

Officer Pitt sighed. "This seemed like such a good idea," he said.

"Sly knew. I wonder who tipped him off," Brad said.

The grocer came out. He helped a man

nearby. Then he turned to Meg. "May I help you?" he asked.

Meg had to do something. So she reached for a handful of apples. "I'll take these," she said.

The grocer put them in a bag. "That will be a dollar and twenty cents," he told her.

Meg reached in her purse. Her eyes grew big. "My wallet is not there! It's been stolen! I checked it after Sly walked past. So it has happened in the last few minutes," she gasped.

"Sly must have a partner," Brad said.

Officer Pitt sighed. "I hope you're right. It's either that or Sly isn't the pickpocket after all," he told them.

CHAPTER 6

The Uniform

Brad and Meg gave the two-way radios to Officer Pitt. Then they went to Aunt Lill's house. Lill helped Meg take off the make-up.

Brad leaned back in a chair. "Lots of people were around those boxes. Any one of them could have grabbed the wallet," he told her.

"I didn't feel anything," Meg said.

"Of course you didn't. Pickpockets are fast and smooth," Brad said.

"It could have been the grocer. He waited on a man right beside me," Meg said.

"Or it could have been the man. He had time to snatch it," Brad told her.

Aunt Lill held up her hands. "Stop! You two are going around in circles. Nothing can be done tonight. So just relax," she said.

"That's hard to do," Brad told her.

Aunt Lill's face lit up. "I know what. There's a play I want to see. And I have two extra tickets. It's across town. Brad, there are some snacks in the kitchen. Meanwhile, I'll get Meg cleaned up. Then we'll have dinner. After that we'll go to the play. What do you think of that?" she asked.

"It sounds great to me," Brad told her.

"Me, too," Meg added.

Two hours later the three of them were at the play. They found their seats and sat down.

Meg smiled at Aunt Lill. "This was a good idea. I feel better already," she said.

The curtain went up. And the play began. It was a mystery. The hero was trying to save the pretty girl. So he offered to help her. Now a policeman walked on the stage.

Meg nudged Brad's arm. "That's Officer Pitt. He must act in his spare time," she said.

"Yes, he must. But why is he wearing his own police uniform? See, that's his badge," Brad said.

Now Officer Pitt is putting a two-way radio on the hero. That's the same radio he gave me," Meg added.

Brad stared at it. Meg was right. It was the same radio. All of a sudden Brad felt like a light went off in his mind. He looked at Meg. Her eyes were wide, too.

"Are you thinking what I'm thinking?" he asked.

Meg nodded. "Yes, I am. And it all fits," she said.

Brad hurried to the lobby. He phoned his friend, Sergeant Ward. "Does the Star City Police have an Officer Pitt?" he asked.

"No, we don't," Sergeant Ward told him.

CHAPTER 7

The Last Theft

The play was over. Brad, Meg, and Aunt Lill left. They went to the cafe next door.

Sergeant Ward was waiting for them. "What's this all about?" he wanted to know.

Brad and Meg took turns. They told Sergeant Ward about Sly and the wallets he took.

"I saw Sly take the first one. But Officer Pitt searched him and found nothing," Meg said.

"The wallet was in Sly's pocket. Officer Pitt just told us it wasn't," Brad said.

Aunt Lill frowned. "So Officer Pitt isn't really a policeman?" she asked.

"No, he isn't," Sergeant Ward said.

Brad spoke up. "The program listed him as Max Pitt. He's an actor. I asked some questions in the lobby. This play has been on for a few weeks. That's when Max Pitt got his costume," he said.

"So Max wore it over to Riddle Street. That's where Sly was picking pockets. The two of them had a great team. That's why my act didn't work. Max Pitt had warned Sly," Meg said.

"That's right. It was Max who later took your wallet. He and I were standing beside you. That's when it happened," Brad said.

"I hope they go to jail," Aunt Lill said.

Sergeant Ward frowned. "We can get Max for acting like an officer. But we can't prove the men stole the wallets," he said.

"It's time for me to go undercover again," Meg told them.

Brad shook his head. "Sly and Max Pitt would know you this time," he said.

"That's true," Sergeant Ward told her.

"They won't know me. My home is near the market. I want it safe," Aunt Lill said.

So it was set for the next afternoon. And Aunt Lill wasn't the only one undercover. Sergeant Ward dressed like a homeless man. He sat on the sidewalk near the market.

Brad wore a two-way radio. Aunt Lill had the other one. He hid behind a bush and watched the street.

Max Pitt was down the block. He wore his police uniform. Sly Bragg stood in a door. He watched the people in front of the market.

Now an old woman came down the street. She went to the market.

Brad knew this was Aunt Lill. He spoke in his radio. "Sly has spotted you. He's behind you. Yes, he's reaching in your purse. Now he has your wallet," Brad said.

"Help! Police!" Aunt Lill screamed.

Sly started running. So did Brad. Sly turned down the alley and headed for the wall.

41

Sly turned down the alley and headed for the wall.
Meg popped over the top. "Surprise!" she shouted.

Meg popped over the top. "Surprise!" she shouted.

Sly turned back. But Brad stood there.

Max Pitt ran up. "Good job, Brad. Let's hope we find the wallet this time," he said.

"You will," Meg told him.

Max Pitt searched Sly. Then he shook his head. "No wallet," he said.

Sergeant Ward hurried up and flashed his badge. He stepped up to Sly and pulled the wallet from his pocket.

"Both of you are under arrest," Sergeant Ward said.

Aunt Lill waited in front of the market. Gertie and Ed Stokes stood beside her.

"Lill told us she was going undercover. Ed and I decided we should be brave, too. So we're here to write out reports on Sly," Gertie told Sergeant Ward.

The grocer rushed out. "I want to write a report on Officer Pitt. He made threats to me. See and say nothing. Or he would wreck my market. I was scared," he said.

"That wraps it up. Riddle Street will be safe again," Sergeant Ward told them.

Brad and Meg told everyone goodbye. Then they headed back to the News.

"What a week!" Meg said.

Brad grinned. "You can't tell what will happen when you go to a flower show," he said.